My STORY
David
My fight with Goliath!

Written by Fiona Boon.

Illustrated by Nadine Wickenden.

make
believe
ideas

My STORY

Hi, I'm David! Before we **start**, I want you to meet some of the **people** in my story.

ME

This is me! I'm an **Israelite** shepherd boy. I use my **sling** and **stones** to **protect** Dad's sheep from **wolves** and **lions**.

This is my **dad**, Jesse. He is the **best farmer** in all of **Bethlehem**!

DAD

SAMUEL

Samuel is a very, very **old** man. People say he is **wise**. He talks to God a **lot**.

King Saul is very **important**. He is **king** of all the **Israelites**.

POSH BEARD

HUGE TEETH

Goliath is a HUGE **Philistine** warrior. All the **Israelites** are **scared** of him — except **me**!

BIG, UGLY TOES

3

One **evening** when I came **home**,
I found Samuel talking to my dad.
They **called** me over, and Samuel
poured **special oil** all over my **head**!
I thought this was WEIRD, but
Dad looked really **pleased** and **proud**.
He said that God had **chosen** me
and that **one day** I would be king.

5

My **older brothers** were really **jealous**, but they had no time to **tease** me, 'cause we were at war with the Philistines and they had to go off to **fight**. They left in a **hurry**, so a few days later, Dad sent me to take them **fresh food** and **clothes**.

FOOD AND CLOTHES

When I **arrived**, all the soldiers were **listening** to this **challenge**: "Israelites! Why are you **waiting** for a **battle**? **Choose** your best man to **fight** me. If he **wins**, you can rule over us, but if I **beat** him, you will all become our slaves. **Ha, ha, ha**!"

LOTS OF WEAPONS

9

I **squeezed** through the crowd until I could **see**. A HUGE **soldier** stood there, shouting. He wore shiny armour and had a **sharp-looking** sword.

PHILISTINES' CAMP

"WOW! Who's **that**?" I asked.

"GOLIATH," said one of the **soldiers**.

"Whoever **beats** him will **marry** the king's **daughter** and be rich!"

11

I **thought** that would be **pretty** cool, so I asked why **no one** had come **forward** to fight him yet.

The soldier **laughed**: "Are you blind? **Everyone's** too scared!"

"**I'm** not scared," I said, a bit too **loudly**.

"I'm not a **great soldier**, but I have killed LIONS before."

KING SAUL'S TENT

13

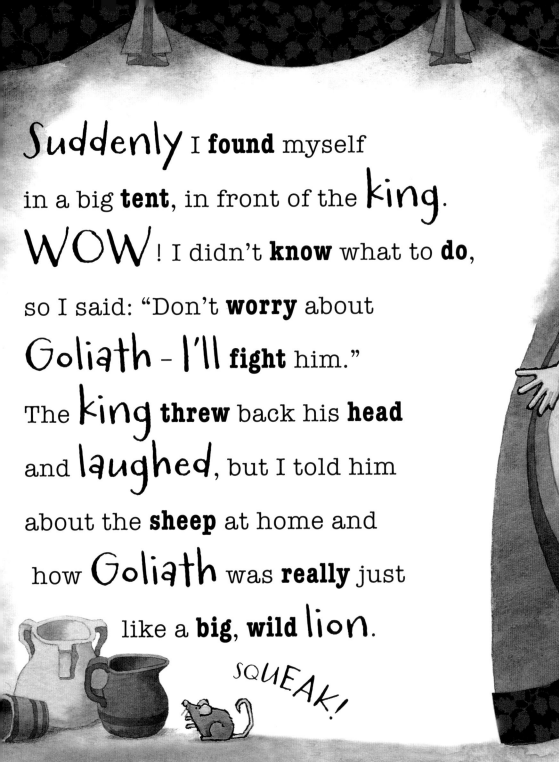

Suddenly I **found** myself in a big **tent**, in front of the king. WOW! I didn't **know** what to **do**, so I said: "Don't **worry** about Goliath – I'll **fight** him." The king **threw** back his **head** and laughed, but I told him about the **sheep** at home and how Goliath was **really** just like a **big, wild** lion.

SQUEAK!

15

Next thing I knew, I was **trembling** in my **tunic** and **sandals** in front of Goliath. He ROARED and **ran** straight at me! I **prayed** to God for **help**, slipped a **smooth stone** into my **sling** and let it FLY through the **air**.

SHARP SWORD

BLEAT!

BLEAT!

17

It was a **perfect** shot and landed, SMACK, in the middle of Goliath's **forehead**. God had **answered** my **prayer**! Goliath **fell** to the **ground** with a THUD and I **ran** over, **grabbed** his **big** sword and chopped off his **head**. His **huge**, **ugly** face was **twice** as **big** as mine.

UGLY FEET

BLEAT!

BLEAT!

20

RUN, MEN!

Just then I **heard** a great RUMBLING **behind** me. I **looked** around and **saw** that the Philistines were **running away**! We cheered and **ran after** them. We **beat** them easily, of course, and it was **all** because God **helped** me when it **mattered** most.

21

My Sticker Journal

Can you remember my story? Use the **stickers** to complete my journal.

Goliath was **big** and **strong**.

ROAR!

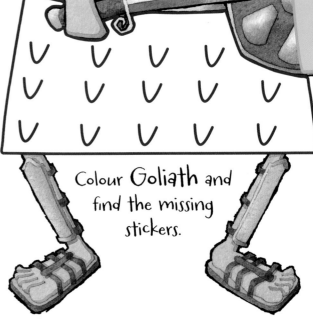

Colour Goliath and find the missing stickers.

No one in the **army** of **brave** soldiers would **fight** Goliath!

22

I **used** my **sling** to fight.

Add some colour.

I **fought** in many battles for King Saul.

I killed Goliath with a **single** stone.

Happy times!

I married King Saul's daughter, **Michal**.

23

God made me **king**.

I had a **son** called
Solomon.

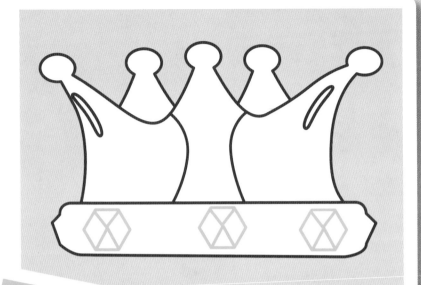

Colour the crown and use your stickers to decorate it.

My son, **Solomon**, is going
to be the new **king**!